Friends Who Share

by Tracy Gallo
illustrated by Karen Dugan

HOUGHTON MIFFLIN

BOSTON

Printed in China

ISBN-13: 978-0-547-02911-5
ISBN-10: 0-547-02911-X

5 6 7 8 9 0940 15 14 13
4500396734

apple

Jan and I like to eat apples.

Jan has an apple to eat.

I want to eat the apple, too.

apple

Jan eats the apple.

I can eat the apple, too!

bike

Jan and I like to ride bikes.

Jan has a bike to ride.

I want to ride the bike, too.

Jan rides the bike.

I can ride the bike, too!

ball

Jan and I like to play ball.

Jan wants to play ball.

I want to play ball, too.

Jan plays ball.

I can play ball, too!

book

Jan and I like to read books.

Jan has a book to read.

I want to read
the book, too.

Jan reads a book to me.

I read a book to Jan!

Responding

What is this book mostly about?
What details tell about this idea?
Make a word web.

Talk About It

Text to Text Think of a different story about friends. How do the friends share with each other? How do they help each other?

✔ **TARGET SKILL** Main Idea

Tell important ideas and details about a topic.

✔ **TARGET STRATEGY** Summarize

Stop to tell important ideas as you read.

GENRE Informational text gives facts about a topic.